IT'$ MY MONEY

VOLUME 2

A Guided Journal to Help You Manage Your Finances

Patrina Dixon

Published by Destination Elevation Publishing
ISBN: 978-1737587002

THIS JOURNAL BELONGS TO:

_____

ACKNOWLEDGMENTS

I am so grateful for the success of It'$ My Money...a guided journal to help you manage your finances Vol1. Those that read it shared how it has helped them get grounded on several finance topics. I am truly thankful for the many people that purchased it either for themselves, a teen in their life, a classroom, or students in their programs. I appreciate each and every one of you!

I continue to trust in God for the many blessings Vol 1 has brought to me and my business. I also now own the official trademark for It'$ My Money ™.

I especially want to thank my supportive family: Fred (my loving husband), Kelli, (my beautiful daughter) and Mildred (the best mom in the entire world). I am also thankful to my other family members, friends, leaders of organizations and schools, and all of the individuals that purchased or referred others to buy the book.

Those that have encouraged me along the way, or gave me feedback, it helped me and was used to create Vol2. It warms my heart when I think about the support from so many of the It'$ My Money™ mission to help empower as many individuals as possible to become more financially literate and have financial freedom.

DISCLAIMER

Concepts, stories and content is for information purposes.
I encourage you to seek a professional if you need advice.

TABLE OF CONTENTS

I remember receiving my first check. It was $75.17 but I was happy. I was proud of myself. You know...that feeling that you accomplished something, you can't define it but deep down inside you are patting yourself on the back. The feeling had swelled up inside of me because I had earned my first check and I could yell out...It was My Money! I remember riding my bike to the bank early Saturday morning. I made sure I was waiting for the manager to open up so I could deposit my money into my account. Not long after making the deposit, I made my way to the mall. I wanted to find a special gift for my Mom. It truly meant the world to me to be able to give her something with my money. I soon had spent $60 of the $75.17. It was my money but was I spending it quicker than the amount of time it took me to earn it.

Fast forward, I had the most amazing opportunity to attend the Morehouse College in Atlanta, GA. While I was a student at Morehouse, I majored in Business Marketing. I had this idea in my head that I would climb the corporate ladder and become a fortune 500 CEO. While in college, I was an Inroads Intern and earned Internships with Liberty Mutual, Kraft Foods, and Aetna. In these internships, I was making $750-$1000 a week and even had a company car all at the age of 18 and 19 years old. Nonetheless, I was still spending money quicker than it took to earn it. I was young and attempting to live my best life with my money. Like many people my age, I was not even remotely close to thinking about saving, budgeting, investing and many other ways to be financially fit.

Upon graduation from Morehouse, I had job offers ranging from $50,000-$60,000 with a $10,000 signing bonus. I was going to take on the corporate world and climb the ladder of corporate success! While attending Morehouse, I developed a love for business as well as a passion for education and youth development. I turned down all the job offers to take a position as a teaching fellow in Massachusetts at the Fessenden School where I was going to make $25,000 for the year and only be paid once a month. An important lesson I can share from making that decision is that as you walk your path in life is that you should chase the vision and not the money and the money will end up chasing you. In making the all-important choice of following my passion and purpose, I was still left with the fact that I would only be making $25,000 a year.

This new salary was a drastic shift from what life had been like over the last four years since my first check at McDonald's. In pursuing my passion, I also made the best financial decision for my life without even knowing it. Once I started the teaching fellowship, I was making about $1500 a month. I had an estimated fixed cost per month of about $1200. After all expenses, I had $300 to my name each month. This experience forced me to learn about how I can make My Money work for me.

17 years since that first check and 12 years since the teaching fellowship in Massachusetts, I no longer live paycheck to paycheck. I have a job that pays me every two weeks, but I have become so financially stable that I don't usually remember that it is payday. My investment portfolio is at an all-time high and my savings account would allow me to quit work for an entire year. All these tips, tricks, and best practices are inside the It's My Money Journal. I didn't know Patrina in my early 20's when I needed her and this journal. I have since become a fan and client; it has only accelerated my growth.

The journey to becoming financially fit and focused is a hard one. It is going to push your limits. It's going to cause you to undergo some serious self-reflection. I can promise that on the other side of the anxiety is joy, happiness, and relaxation that you deserve! I have experienced the It's My Money Journey and I feel liberated every day! If you are reading this foreword, then you have made the right choice. Let's take the first step so you can be financially fit and liberated too!

Brandon M. Frame
Founder, TheBlackManCan
Director of Social Emotional Learning, The Urban Assembly
Author, My First Tie

Dear Financial Scholars,

This journal is about you and your money. It is purposely designed to provide you with practical information based on research and knowledge received from many like you. I've had the pleasure of working with so many people across the world that helped to shape the content of this volume. I hope it will encourage and inspire you to manage your money - at your own pace. Remember It'$ your money! Please don't compare your money journey to anyone else's. Vol1 was designed to introduce the money topics and this 2nd volume, in the 3-part series, gives more depth and takes you from the money you make to preparing for your first big purchases.

The journal is structured with information on relevant financial topics, short summaries, real-life examples, inspirational quotes throughout, lined pages for journaling, a glossary in the back, and thought-provoking questions to help you better plan your financial future. The format had you in mind as this is a great resource to revisit as you approach some of the stages when you have to make a financial decision.

Please keep in mind, everyone's journey is different and unique. Therefore, no two will be alike. Be confident and consistent with your goals for your money. Document your progress as you go along your journey.

The journey of financial success is never-ending. Soak up the knowledge and begin adding them to your daily routines. Start now. I am confident you will see large gains! Let's start with my sharing my story.

Financially fit,

Patrina Dixon
The It'$ My Money Lady

When I am interviewed about what I do, I am often asked, "Why do you do what you do?" Or "Why did you choose to teach personal finance?" My answer to both is multifaceted as there are so many reasons why I do this work. Most of it stems from me making some absolutely horrible decisions with my money, such as spending it before I received it, ignoring bills, and buying things that made me feel good for a minute. I had several credit cards but didn't always pay them all or on time. I owned a home, car, and many material things, but no real assets and I had no money saved so I was one paycheck from everything falling apart.

Then the ah ha moments began. What am I doing? I work hard, make good money and yet, I don't own anything. Then I became interested in learning how to do right by my money. How to be a better steward of my money. I watched and listened to the financial experts of that time. I became a diligent and focused student of "getting my money in order." I was committed to getting my money right. Yes, I made mistakes while I was learning but I kept trying and trying until I got it right. I got better and better each time.

Once I got it right, I wanted to teach EVERYONE how to do it. It was a mind shift and mastering some skills and tactics and I started seeing the difference in aspects of my finances. The funny thing during this time is that I made the same money but did better things with it. I received financial management skills from Cornell University and became certified as a Financial Education Instructor by the National Financial Education Council and the It'$ My Money™ mission began. I believe I am called to do this. I am most fulfilled while doing it and have a smile in my heart when people transform their mindset about money and have the ah ha moment when they realize how beautiful life can be when you master your money skills.

Now, let's Go!!

EMPLOYMENT

As you think about how to manage your money, you first have to have money. The most common way people start to have money is by earning it through their job. There are also a lot of people jumping right into starting their own business as an entrepreneur. We will go over entrepreneurship and side hustles in a later chapter.

It is important when you start working for an employer, that you understand all parts of your paycheck. I have met with many people about money since Vol 1 of It'$ My Money was published and learned that many don't understand each part nor knew there was a difference between gross and net pay. So many get their 1st "real" job and give their employer, either directly, or online, a bank account number. This is usually a checking account with a routing number, to have their entire paycheck deposited. The intent of this journal is to give you tips designed to get you started off on a great financial foundation therefore the goal is to start saving money as soon as you start earning money. Instead of giving one account number, provide checking and a savings account number. Have a set amount to go into your savings account and the balance of your paycheck to go into your checking account. The goal is to automate your savings and forget it. This is the deposit structure that you want to continue to set for your first job and any others thereafter.

Ok, let's touch on the amount you earn. There is gross pay and net pay. Gross is before any applicable deductions. Net pay is after deductions. The net is what will actually go into your account(s). Deductions are things like taxes or if you have a portion to pay to have access to medical or dental benefits. Depending on your age you may have little to no deductions. Check out this sample paycheck stub from an employer.

ABC Company 79-8823922
2020 Joe B Jackson Parkway,
Murfreesboro, TN 37127

Earnings Statement

Stub Number: 1694

Employee Info			SSN	Pay Schedule	Pay Period		Pay Date
John Employee Id: 6437898 402 John Dodd Road, Spartanburg, SC 29303			XXX-XX-4639	Weekly	Aug 03, 2020 to Aug 10, 2020		Aug 16, 2020

Earnings	Rate	Units	Total	YTD	Taxes / Deductions	Current	YTD
Overtime (1.5X)	$375.00	10.00 hrs	$3,750.00	$127,500.00	Federal Withholding	$919.33	$31,257.22
Tips	-	-	$500.00	$17,000.00	FICA - Social Security	$0.00	$0.00
					FICA - Medicare	$61.63	$2,095.42

YTD Gross	YTD Taxes / Deductions	YTD Net Pay	Gross	Taxes / Deductions	Net Pay
$144,500.00	$33,352.64	$111,147.36	$4,250.00	$980.96	$3,269.04

The other thing that you may be asked to complete is a W4 form. This form is the Employee's Withholding Certificate, and it is used by employers to determine the amount of taxes that will be withheld from your paycheck. The W4 has directions on how to complete each field. Be sure you fully understand everything that is on the form. If you are unsure, then you may want to get some help.

If you do not complete a W4 form, then you will still get your paycheck. However, your employer will deduct the highest amount allowed by law and return the form with your applicable information and preferences.

After the end of the calendar year, you will receive a W2 tax form from your employer. Typically, employers distribute them to the employees online, if this is an option, or include them with a paycheck. Some employers may even mail them to you. For example, for any work from January-December of 2019, you will get a W2 in January of 2020. It will have how much money you made in 2019 and the total amount of your deductions.

You may also receive income as a contractor or freelance worker. In those cases you may be asked to do assignments or tasks such as administrative task being a Virtual Assistant or managing someone social media sites as a Social Media Manager or building and maintaining a website for a small business owner. The person you are providing the service to or for may ask for a W9 with your business information on it and at the end of the year, depending on the accumulated amount they will provide you with a 1099 form for your taxes.

Below are some action steps each time you start working for an employer:

1. Review all paperwork before signing.
2. Give account information for both your savings and checking accounts.
3. Give a set dollar amount or percentage that you want to be deposited in your savings account and have the rest deposited in your checking account.
4. Complete a W4, sign it and return it to the employer.

Form W-4	**Employee's Withholding Certificate**	OMB No. 1545-0074
(Rev. December 2020) Department of the Treasury Internal Revenue Service	▶ Complete Form W-4 so that your employer can withhold the correct federal income tax from your pay. ▶ Give Form W-4 to your employer. ▶ Your withholding is subject to review by the IRS.	**2021**

Step 1:
Enter Personal Information

(a) First name and middle initial — Last name

(b) Social security number

Address

▶ Does your name match the name on your social security card? If not, to ensure you get credit for your earnings, contact SSA at 800-772-1213 or go to www.ssa.gov

City or town, state, and ZIP code

(c)
☐ Single or Married filing separately
☐ Married filing jointly or Qualifying widow(er)
☐ Head of household (Check only if you're unmarried and pay more than half the costs of keeping up a home for yourself and a qualifying individual.)

Complete Steps 2–4 ONLY if they apply to you; otherwise, skip to Step 5. See page 2 for more information on each step, who can claim exemption from withholding, when to use the estimator at www.irs.gov/W4App, and privacy.

Step 2:
Multiple Jobs or Spouse Works

Complete this step if you (1) hold more than one job at a time, or (2) are married filing jointly and your spouse also works. The correct amount of withholding depends on income earned from all of these jobs.

Do **only one** of the following.

(a) Use the estimator at www.irs.gov/W4App for most accurate withholding for this step (and Steps 3–4); or

(b) Use the Multiple Jobs Worksheet on page 3 and enter the result in Step 4(c) below for roughly accurate withholding; or

(c) If there are only two jobs total, you may check this box. Do the same on Form W-4 for the other job. This option is accurate for jobs with similar pay; otherwise, more tax than necessary may be withheld . . . . . ▶ ☐

TIP: To be accurate, submit a 2021 Form W-4 for all other jobs. If you (or your spouse) have self-employment income, including as an independent contractor, use the estimator.

Complete Steps 3–4(b) on Form W-4 for only ONE of these jobs. Leave those steps blank for the other jobs. (Your withholding will be most accurate if you complete Steps 3–4(b) on the Form W-4 for the highest paying job.)

Step 3:
Claim Dependents

If your total income will be $200,000 or less ($400,000 or less if married filing jointly):

Multiply the number of qualifying children under age 17 by $2,000 ▶ $

Multiply the number of other dependents by $500 . . . . ▶ $

Add the amounts above and enter the total here . . . . **3** $

Step 4 (optional):
Other Adjustments

(a) **Other income (not from jobs).** If you want tax withheld for other income you expect this year that won't have withholding, enter the amount of other income here. This may include interest, dividends, and retirement income . . . . **4(a)** $

(b) **Deductions.** If you expect to claim deductions other than the standard deduction and want to reduce your withholding, use the Deductions Worksheet on page 3 and enter the result here . . . . **4(b)** $

(c) **Extra withholding.** Enter any additional tax you want withheld each **pay period** . **4(c)** $

Step 5:
Sign Here

Under penalties of perjury, I declare that this certificate, to the best of my knowledge and belief, is true, correct, and complete.

▶ _____
Employee's signature (This form is not valid unless you sign it.)

▶ _____
Date

Employers Only

Employer's name and address

First date of employment

Employer identification number (EIN)

For Privacy Act and Paperwork Reduction Act Notice, see page 3.

Cat. No. 10220Q

Form **W-4** (2021)

It'$ My Money

22222	a Employee's social security number 123-45-6789	OMB No. 1545-0008		
b Employer identification number (EIN) 11-2233444		1 Wages, tips, other compensation $47,000.00	2 Federal income tax withheld $4,700.00	
c Employer's name, address, and ZIP code		3 Social security wages $50,000.00	4 Social security tax withheld $3,100.00	
Big Employer 123 Easy Street Washington, DC 12345		5 Medicare wages and tips $50,000.00	6 Medicare tax withheld $725.00	
		7 Social security tips	8 Allocated tips	
d Control number		9	10 Dependent care benefits	
e Employee's first name and initial Last name Suff.		11 Nonqualified plans	12a	
		13 Statutory employee / Retirement plan / Third-party sick pay	12b	
Irma B. Taxpayer 456 Main Street Philadelphia, PA 12345		14 Other	12c	
			12d	
f Employee's address and ZIP code				

15 State	Employer's state ID number	16 State wages, tips, etc.	17 State income tax	18 Local wages, tips, etc.	19 Local income tax	20 Locality name
PA	55-222222222	$50,000.00	$1,535.00	$50,000.00	$800.00	TGP

Form **W-2** Wage and Tax Statement   2020   Department of the Treasury—Internal Revenue Service
Copy 1—For State, City, or Local Tax Department

5

> "Wealth consists not in having great possessions, but in having few wants." - Epictetus

"A dream doesn't become reality through magic. It takes sweat, determination, and hard work." - Colin Powell

> "Too many people spend money to impress people they don't even know." - Will Smith

It'$ My Money

BANKING

In Vol1, I shared that people often spend cash faster when it is in their hands, wallet, or pocket. This can lead to forgetting how much that was spent, where, and when. It's much easier to manage your finances when you have and use a checking and savings accounts. Banks and credit unions are places where you can store your money. Both offer various accounts, such as checking, savings, money market, and certificate of deposits. Each has both brick-and-mortar locations, are available online, and has apps, so you can bank on the go. The biggest differences between the two is the eligibility requirements, the number of physical locations, fees, and interest earned.

Let's start with banks:

Banks have several locations, statewide and in some cases across the country. You can open an account as long as you meet the age and minimal deposit amount. Banks are for profit, which means they are in business to make money. One of the ways they make money is by charging fees for several things like:

- Going below the minimum dollar balance in your account
- Using overdraft protection
- Bounced checks, which is a term when you do not have sufficient funds in your account for a transaction you made

- Using an ATM to get money from a machine that is not from your bank. Example, you have an account with one bank, and you use the ATM at a different bank, you will be charged a fee

You want to ensure the bank you choose is FDIC insured. FDIC insured means the federal government will insure your funds up to $250,000 per depositor, per bank, per ownership category.

Now let's compare credit unions:

Credit Unions offer the same type of accounts as banks. The biggest difference is credit unions are not-for-profit. The not-for-profit means they operate in a different fashion.

- Most require certain eligibility rules like where you live, if you or a family member work a certain company, go to a certain school or worship in the area.
- Their fees are usually less
- They only have a few brick-and-mortar locations.

You want to ensure you choose a credit union that is NCUA insured. This means the National Credit Union Administration insures up to $250,000, the same way FDIC does for banks.

When it comes to banking, you may be thinking, how do I start? Should I have an account at a bank or credit union? Choose what is best for you. Here are some things to consider:

- Is it FDIC or NCUA insured?
- What is the interest rate your money will earn?
- What are the fees of the various transactions?
- Do you have to go into a brick-and-mortar location or is there an app?

- Would you prefer an internet only based account?
- Do you want easy access to see your balances (the money you have in the bank)?

The bank or credit union's website will have details on their accounts. You want to review, get your questions answered before making a final decision.

There are several great online only banking options. They don't have brick and mortar locations, so their overhead costs are lower. Therefore, they can afford to offer higher interest and less fees. Now don't confuse this with brick-and-mortar banks that give you access to your account online or via their app. Online only means just that, only, not in addition to.

Let's dive into checking accounts.

A checking account is a type of account that can help you track the movement of your money. Many use it as an "operational account." Meaning the money that is deposited into the checking account is not meant to stay it is meant to pay bills. Typically, there are frequent transactions like deposits and withdrawals in and out of a checking account. These transactions can be made in the bank with the teller, online, via a mobile app, with a check, or online transfer.

With a checking account, you will receive a debit card. The debit card gives you the ability to make purchases in a store, online, and make a withdrawal or deposit from an automatic teller machine (ATM). You will need a four-digit pin specific to your debit card. Once you choose a pin do not share it with anyone.

The debit card that you are given with your checking account looks like a credit card, but it is not, and it operates differently than a credit card. Credit cards will be explained in chapter 5.

I know you're probably thinking, "Checks are so outdated! Who uses checks nowadays?" Well, according to federalreserve.gov in 2020, over 3 million commercial checks will have been collected in 2020. Sure, it is declining but still happening, so it is good to learn how to manage a checking account and how to write checks against the fund in your checking account. Checks are legal documents that can be used like cash, typically for paying for larger expenses. Knowing how to write a check is a necessary fundamental financial skill. When writing a check or using your debit card, you should track the transaction in the check register that the bank provides to you and update the new balance in the check register as well. The check register has space for your current balance, date for traction and a place for the updated balance after you track the transaction. Some transactions will be reduced from the prior balance, and some added. This is called *balancing your checkbook.*

Balancing your checkbook means making note of how your funds are moving in and out of your account. Your bank will keep track of this as well, however, some transactions are not as immediate and timely. For example, if you write a check to a family member and they don't cash it for a week, the bank does not know you wrote that check so your bank balance will not automatically be reduced. At least not until the person cashes it. That is why it is important that you write it down, so you will not forget things like checks you wrote but have not yet been cashed. If you always keep track of your transactions consistently, then there should be no surprises when you review your monthly statement. If your statement has items that you are not familiar with, then contact your bank as soon as possible.

If you write a check for an amount that is more than you have in your account, then the bank will deny it for insufficient funds. That means you didn't have sufficient funds to cover the transaction and they will charge you a fee. If you wrote a check to a company or store, then they may charge you a fee as well. If you wrote a check to a person, they may be upset with you as they may also be assessed a fee on their side depending on how they cashed the check. That is why it is important for you to track all of your expenses to ensure you are not writing checks for money that is not in the bank. Also, if you happen to do so, ensure you track any fees in your check register so that you know exactly how much you actually have in the bank. Also checks should be written in ink not pencil. Below shows you the various pieces of vital information that are a part of a check.

Remember once you sign your name and give it to the store or someone you own the outcome of the check.

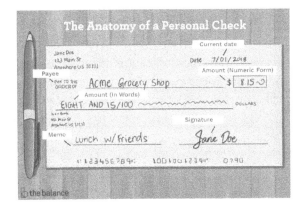

Below are components of a check.

Upper left-hand corner: This should have your 1st and last name and complete mailing address.

Upper right-hand corner: The check #

Underneath the check # The date. This should be the date you write the check. It should not be a future date.

Pay to the order of : This is the person or place you are writing the check to.

The line below pay to the order of: This is the dollar amount of the check and must be written in words. Example: Eight and 15/100 not $8.15

Next to the pay to the order of: This is where you would write the pallor amount of the check expressed in a value. example: $8.15

Bottom Left: Memo is to comment on what you wrote the check for, clothes, rent, cell phone bill. This is for your records

Bottom Right: Your signature will always be the bottom right line.

Next Steps: Now try it. Write a check, using the sample below to Sprint for your cell phone bill. There are two samples for you to practice with.

Above the memo line is usually the name of your bank or credit union.

The numbers under the memo line are the routing numbers. The routing numbers are specific and the bank and the numbers under the signature line are unique to your specific account.

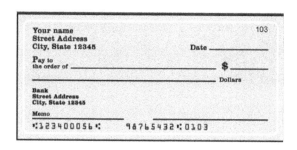

"You want to change things in a big way, you have you make big changes." - Creed II

> "Money is only a tool. It will take you wherever you wish, but it will not replace you as the driver." - Ayn Rand

_____

_____

_____

_____

_____

_____

_____

_____

_____

_____

_____

_____

_____

_____

_____

_____

_____

_____

_____

> Believe you can and you're halfway there. -Theodore Roosevelt

_____

_____

_____

_____

_____

_____

_____

_____

_____

_____

_____

_____

_____

_____

_____

_____

_____

_____

_____

It'$ My Money

BUDGETING

Success involves a plan. Financial plans are known as budgets and oftentimes called spending plans. The goal is to tell your money where to go and not try and remember where it went after it has been spent.

Your personal budget should include the exact amount of your net income NOT your gross income. It should include all of your expenses. Hint, if you have a car with a car payment, you should include your car payment, car insurance and even the gas. Even though gas doesn't have a due date, it is an expense that car owners need to account for in their budget. Some expenses will be the same every month and some will vary depending on usage. The expenses that don't change from month-to-month are called fixed expenses, which are also often referred to as needs, such as your rent and car payment. Then there are flexible expenses, which are also referred to as needs, that occur regularly, but the amount differs based on your usage, like gas and groceries. You have control over flexible expenses. Groceries would be considered a flexible expense because your spending varies based on intake and need. Then there are discretionary expenses. They are what I would say are your wants. Things that fall in discretionary expenses are extra activities, shopping, things like that.

Things to consider when creating a personal budget:

- Decide on the duration of the budget (weekly, bi-weekly, monthly).
- List all of your income.
- List all of your expenses and label them (fixed, flexible, discretionary). Or needs vs wants.
- Review the expenses you listed and adjust where you can.
- Review the budget as often as you receive income. So, if you get paid weekly, review it weekly.

Before spending, ask yourself the following questions: *Is this a want or need? Will this expense take away from my needs? Can I wait to save for this expense?*

Learn the power of delayed gratification. The wants will eventually happen but may not be able to happen immediately. You have to become intimate with your money. Be sure to check your funds before making any decisions. An excellent budget takes into consideration current and future expenses.

Tips for saving dollars on a budget: 1. Automate it. 2. Don't order take out excessively. 3. Get used books when you can and sell them back. 4. Make gifts instead of purchasing them.

Next Steps: Use the previous information to create your budget. A template has been provided for you on the next page. The expenses should not be greater than the income.

SAMPLE BUDGET SHEET

1. INCOME (Net Pay) _____

2. EXPENSES:

	BUDGET (amount planned to pay)	ACTUAL (actually paid)
Saving	_____	_____
Tithes	_____	_____
Cell phone	_____	_____
Transportation	_____	_____
Eating out	_____	_____
Shopping	_____	_____
Toiletries	_____	_____
Nails/Hair	_____	_____
Credit Card	_____	_____
TOTAL	_____	_____

3. AMOUNT LEFT OVER -
Deduct total expenses in section 2 from total income in section 1.

_____   _____

> "The person who doesn't know where his next dollar is coming from usually doesn't know where his last dollar went." - Unknown

_____

_____

_____

_____

_____

_____

_____

_____

_____

_____

_____

_____

_____

_____

_____

_____

_____

_____

_____

_____

> "Save money, and money will save you." - Jamaican Proverb

_____

_____

_____

_____

_____

_____

_____

_____

_____

_____

_____

_____

_____

_____

_____

_____

_____

_____

_____

_____

"I knew if I failed, I wouldn't regret that, but I knew the one thing I might regret is not trying." -Jeff Bezos

SAVING

Saving is about putting money away for future use. People save for many reasons such as vacations, college, to start a business, to buy a house, car, to invest or start an emergency fund.

Brick and mortar banks, credit unions and online only banks are great places to save your money. Examples of brick-and-mortar banks are Chase and Bank of America. Online only banks examples are Capital One 360 performance, Ally, and Marcus by Goldman Sachs. One of my favorite parts about saving money, wherever you save it, is you can earn interest. Interest is money the bank or credit union gives you for keeping your money in there. The longer you keep it in, the more you earn. That is why it is important to find the one that works best for you with the highest interest rate. There are two types of interest: simple and compound. The amount of interest you earn varies by the bank.

Let's explore each type of interest. The 1st is simple interest, which is calculated by using the amount of money you put in the bank times the % of interest your bank or credit union offers.

Example of Simple Interest:
    $100 - The amount you have in the bank
    1% or $1 - The interest offered

Total you now have in the bank is $101. You earned $1 for keeping your money in the bank.

The 2nd is compound interest. That is one of my absolute favorites. It is the opportunity to earn more free money from the bank. It is calculated by using the amount you have in the bank PLUS the simple interest you've earned from the bank. YES, it is free money on top of free money.

Another type of savings' account is a Certificates of Deposit most commonly known as CDs. CDs are best for longer term needs like funding college or buying a house or car. They often require a larger minimum deposit. Additionally, these accounts must be opened for a specific amount of time, known as a term. If you withdraw money before the term is up, then you will incur a penalty. The date at the end of the term is called the maturity date.

Another type of savings' account is a Money Market. This type of savings account allows for limited check writing and withdrawals each month because these accounts usually pay a higher interest over a fixed amount of time.

When choosing a savings account, you want to find one that have the following characteristics:

- No or low fees
- $0 to low opening amount
- No or small minimum balance required each month
- FDIC insured
- Highest interest rate

Just like a checking account, withdrawals, deposits, and transfers can be made using a savings account. You can access your account online, using a mobile app, at the bank, or the ATM.

By now you may have read my story in the beginning of the book. I made a lot of money but had none saved. I had a savings account and would put some in and take it out as fast as I put it in the account. I didn't use it the way a savings account should be used. You should deposit money in and leave it in the account as long as you can. This way it will earn more interest from the bank. A tip to save is, automate it and forget about it. Set an amount that fits within your budget and do that for a period of time. The goal is to increase it. If you are not currently saving money, don't try to have a huge amount. Be sure it fits in your budget, start that way first and let that sit for 90 days, then increase it more after time and then more. As you continue to budget, hopefully your discretionary spending will decrease, and your set savings amount will increase over time.

I wish someone gave me this tip when I was younger.

If you go into the bank and make transactions to deposit money in or withdraw money out of your savings account., you will be asked to complete a slip depending on the transaction. See samples below.

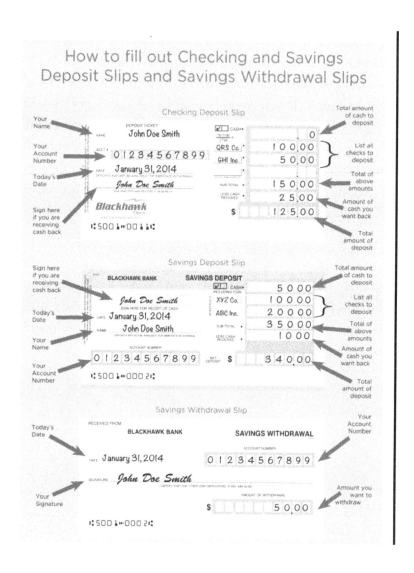

TIP: Online only savings accounts typically offer the highest interest rate than your local bank or credit union. You can compare online only savings accounts on bankrate.com, or nerdwallet.com.

ESSENTIAL QUESTIONS

Apply the information you've learned from the overview when answering the essential questions within the chapter.

1. Why is it important to save?

   _____

   _____

   _____

2. What are the two types of savings accounts?

   _____

   _____

   _____

3. What does compound interest mean?

   _____

   _____

   _____

4. What is a term as it pertains to CDs?

   _____

   _____

   _____

5. What does CD stand for?

   _____

   _____

   _____

> "If you wait to see how much money you have left at the end of the month to put toward savings, the answer may be zero. So, set up an automated monthly transfer from your checking to savings account." - Suze Orman

---

"Save your money. You're going to need twice as much money in your old age as you think." – Michael Caine

_____

_____

_____

_____

_____

_____

_____

_____

_____

_____

_____

_____

_____

_____

_____

_____

_____

_____

| "The way to build your savings is by spending less each month." - Suze Orman

_____

_____

_____

_____

_____

_____

_____

_____

_____

_____

_____

_____

_____

_____

_____

_____

_____

_____

_____

$ FUNDING COLLEGE

Now this is one many want to know about, parents and students alike. There are a few options.

The best way is to consistently get good grades, do community service and have a well-rounded profile and maybe you can finance college with scholarships and grants. These are dollars you don't have to pay back.

Let's break each of these down.

Scholarships:
- A financial award
- Earned by academic, artistic, or athletic merit
- Application-based
- Can be provided by several institutions like businesses, philanthropists, organizations, foundations, and unions.
- "Gift aid" you do NOT need to pay

Here are some of the common places to find scholarships
- College Board
- Scholly
- Sallie Mae
- United Negro College Fund
- Unigo
- Scholarship Owl

Here are some tips to each scholarship dollars:
- ☐ Be a well-rounded student
- ☐ Be in good academic standing
- ☐ Join school/community clubs and organizations
- ☐ Try a sport
- ☐ Work (if you can)
- ☐ Stay involved
- ☐ Get recommendations
- ☐ Get recommendations from teachers/faculty/mentors (anyone outside of family) that can attest to your character (personally and/or academically)
- ☐ Submit your applications early and consistently
- ☐ Remember: "Early is on time, on time is late, and late is unacceptable!"
- ☐ Write an outstanding essay
- ☐ Be sure to write an essay that sets you apart from the rest
- ☐ Stick to the question! Stay on topic
- ☐ Don't ramble, get straight to the point
- ☐ Apply for as many as you can
- ☐ The more applications you complete, the more money you might receive
- ☐ Don't Get Discouraged
- ☐ If you didn't get the scholarship or didn't hear back, don't give up. There's many more out there for you.
- ☐ Don't Look Past Anything
- ☐ No scholarship amount is too big or too small. Every dollar counts.
- ☐ 10 $500 scholarships add up quickly. Do not ignore the small ones.

Grants are financial awards usually based on financial need. They are also need-grants usually come from the federal or state government, colleges, or universities

Another option for funding college is Federal Student Aid (FSA).

FSA is:
- Largest supplier of student financial aid
- Assists both undergraduate and graduate students
- Provides loans, grants, and work study programs

Through FSA, you can fill out the Free Application for Student Aid (FAFSA) form, which determines eligibility for different financial aid packages.

- FAFSA basic eligibility requirements
- Present financial aid
- U.S. citizen or eligible non-citizen
- Enrolled in an eligible degree program at a college, university, or career school
- Other special circumstances might influence your package

Another option is Student Loans. Loans are the most common form of financial aid that FSA provides, all given under the William D. Ford Federal Direct Loan Program. The U.S Department of Education is your lender.

There are two types of student loans
1. Federal student loan (funded by the government)
2. Private student loan (lended by private institutions like banks, credit unions, state agencies, and schools)

Let's start with federal loans.

- These loans aren't due until after you graduate or leave school
- Interest rate is fixed and lower than private loans
- You don't need a credit check to qualify (except for PLUS loans)
- Government pays for interest on your loans while you're in school (subsidized loans)

There are a few types of federal student loans
- Direct subsidized loan
- Loans for undergraduate students that display a financial need to cover college/career school costs
- Direct unsubsidized loan
- Loans for undergraduate, graduate, and professional students; eligibility NOT based on financial need
- Direct PLUS loan
- Loans for graduate students and professional students, OR parents with dependent undergraduate students

Now let's review private loans.
- May require payments while you're in school
- Interest rates can be fixed, or they can vary (could be higher or lower than federal student loans)
- Require established credit or a cosigner
- More often unsubsidized, meaning you are responsible for paying interest

FAFSA refund checks should not be spent freely UNLESS you don't have debt or have graduated. If you have debt or more years to college to finish, then a good option would be to put towards one of those. I encourage you to carefully check out the salient points outlined below and/or check out the source noted beneath.

- The excess money given back to you from your financial aid package after your tuition, fees, and room & board have been paid for
- "When a student loan exceeds a student's actual expenses, the result is a financial aid refund. " -fafsapplication.org
- Amount depends on the difference between the total amount of your financial aid package and the total costs of tuition and fees
- Can be disbursed after the add/drop period of classes
- Depending on the school, can be disbursed at the beginning or end of the semester
- Common refund check mistakes
- Not budgeting
- Not saving
- Spending excessively
- Suggestions for your refund check
- Paying for books and campus meal plans.
- Paying for transportation to and from school.
- Picking up additional classes.
- Buying extra research material for classes.
- Using the money to pay for living expenses rather than working full-time.
- Returning a refund check

The excess amount will be removed from a student's financial aid package when the refund check is returned to the Department of Education, which means the student will be free of repaying that amount post-graduation.

source- http://fafsapplication.org/after-completing-the-fafsa/federal-student-aid-refunds/

"Wealth is the ability to fully experience life." - Henry David Thoreau

_____

_____

_____

_____

_____

_____

_____

_____

_____

_____

_____

_____

_____

_____

_____

_____

_____

_____

"Never spend your money before you have earned it." –
Thomas Jefferson

> **"Budget: a mathematical confirmation of your suspicions."** - A.A. Latimer

---

It'$ My Money

$ CREDIT

The best analogy for credit is: You borrow something, like money or things, from somebody and pay it back when you agreed to do so. When you do it well or if you don't do it right, you are rated accordingly. In this chapter we will cover credit history, credit reports ad credit scores at a high level.

Your credit history are the details aligned to how you have repaid each of your creditors. All of your credit history is contained on your credit reports. There are 3 main credit bureaus in the United States. They are Experian, Trans Union and Equifax. Each of them are businesses that receive data from creditors. However it is your responsibility to ensure the data they have is accurate. WHY? Because your future creditors will reply on this information to determine if they will extend credit to you and at which rate. The data they get are things such as:

- First name
- Last name (all in case you have been married or it has changed for other reasons)
- Addresses (any you have had)
- Employers (all)
- Payment history

Each of the bureaus, Experian, Trans Union and Equifax uses that data particularly the payment history to derive a credit score for you on a monthly basis.

There are different scoring methodologies but the FIO is the most commonly used. Even with FICO there are many versions. Below is the most commonly used breakdown of each component of your credit score:

PAYMENT HISTORY (35%)
- Payment information on credit cards, retail accounts, and mortgages
- How overdue delinquent payments are currently or were in the past
- Amount of money still owed on delinquent accounts
- The number of accounts that are being paid as agreed

OUTSTANDING DEBT (30%)
- The amount owed on all accounts
- The amount owed on different types of accounts
- How many accounts have balances
- Credit utilization ratio on revolving accounts
- How much of the installment loan amount is still owed, compared with the original loan amount

CREDIT HISTORY LENGTH (15%)
- How long your credit accounts have been open
- How long specific credit accounts have been open
- • How long it has been since the account has been used

NEW CREDIT (10%)
- How many new accounts you have
- How many recent inquiries you have

- How long it's been since you opened a new account
- Hard Inquiry vs. Soft Inquiry

MISCELLANEOUS FACTORS (10%)
- Revolving Accounts
- Installment Accounts

Credit card companies are great marketers. They will offer you free items, low introductory interest rates, and a lot of points to sign up. Be sure to read the fine print and have your budget and money management mastered before going down the path of using credit.

Your Credit score is a three-digit number which represents how well you have paid your lenders or creditors. A high score is 850 and the lowest is 300.

FICO score ranges:

800 – 850 – Excellent

740 – 799 – Very Good

670 – 739 – Good

580 – 699 – FAIR

300 – 579 – POOR

Hopefully you are reading this BEFORE you start to use credit and can follow these tips.

If you need help building or restoring credit, then a great option is a secured credit card. Secure credit cards allow you to spend a small amount of money such as $200 to secure "your line of credit." It will allow you to purchase up to that dollar amount using that credit card. You are still required to pay monthly by the due date given or you will have to pay interest on any amount owed. This interest is different from interest earned on a savings account. This interest is what the creditor charges you for leaving a balance from one month to the next.

You can go to annualcreditreport.com. Be sure to get a copy of all three reports, one from each bureaus. Go through it with a fine-tooth comb, any errors should be disputed. The way to dispute them is to write a letter to the specific bureau that shows the error.

There are various places that check your credit score, such as when you rent an apartment, buy a car, apply for a loan, and look for certain types of jobs.

TIPS:
1. The higher your credit score - the less you pay on the loan.
2. Always pay bills on time.

You should check your credit report and scores on an annual basis. There are many apps available for you to check your reports and scores. Please take note of the credit score methodology that is used within the app you choose. Some use the Vantage methodology opposed to FICO.

Action Steps:
- Pull your credit report at annualcreditreport.com
- Get your credit score for free at experian.com

"Wealth is not about having a lot of money; it's about having a lot of options." - Chris Rock

> **"Whether you think you can or think you can't - you are right." - Henry Ford**

_____
_____
_____
_____
_____
_____
_____
_____
_____
_____
_____
_____
_____
_____
_____
_____
_____
_____
_____
_____
_____
_____
_____

"I am poor, I can't even pay attention." – Ron Kittle.

_____

_____

_____

_____

_____

_____

_____

_____

_____

_____

_____

_____

_____

_____

_____

_____

_____

_____

_____

_____

_____

_____

INVESTING

Investing in its simplest definition, is taking money along with a risk to make profits. This risk is taken more commonly in a stock market. For example, if you purchase a share of stock in a company at one price, with the hopes that you will earn money and end up with more than your initial purchase. There are a lot of ways to dip your toe into purchasing shares of a company using apps. Some apps even allow you to purchase fractions of a share. A fractional purchase is defined as if one full share costs $50, you can purchase a fraction of that share for $10. The most commonly known apps are Robinhood, Stash, VanGuard, and E*TRADE.

Another form of investment is the purchase of real estate. When you buy property at a certain price, in some cases, you can fix it up and sell it for a profit. Just like in the stock market, you may not be able to sell the property for the price you intend, your profit may be low or you can't sell it at all, therefore you are at a loss. Investing is a risk so you want to be sure you fully understand that amount of money you will use to invest you can afford to lose in case that is the unfortunate result. Once you have decided, do as much research as you can on the way you will invest and what you are going to invest in. A good term to know is portfolio. A portfolio is a range of investments held by you so basically all of the investments that you have make up your portfolio. When you are ready, it may also be a great decision to work with a professional.

There is also now another form of investing, called Crowdfunding. More on this in Vol3.

Another type of investing is in yourself. There may be courses and conferences that are at cost that may give you great information on the entrepreneurial journey you want to start or even if you are already doing it. There also may be a course to perfect your skills. Some of the best investments you can make are in yourself, which translates into your growth as a person, husband, wife, mother, student, business owner or employee.

"Start by doing what's necessary; then do what's possible; and suddenly you are doing the impossible." - Francis of Assisi

"An investment in knowledge pays the best interest." - Benjamin Franklin

_____

_____

_____

_____

_____

_____

_____

_____

_____

_____

_____

_____

_____

_____

_____

_____

_____

_____

_____

_____

_____

_____

"We live by the golden rule. Those that have gold makes the rules". Buzzie Bavasi

$ BUYING A CAR/HOME

Two of the biggest purchases people make are buying a home and a car. A lot of what we talked about earlier in the book such as learning the banking system, knowing how to budget and save, and having a good credit score, will help you with these two transactions. Before you decide to purchase a car or house, you should have good money management skills. If your credit score is not ideal, then it will impact your ability to acquire a car or house, or it will result in you paying more than you should. Let's break down each of these purchases a bit further.

When purchasing a car, you want to do research, compare prices at various locations, and determine the value of the luxuries that each car offers. If you are not a person who listens to music a lot, then purchasing a car with an aux may not make sense. All car prices are negotiable. The salesperson is trying to sell the car at the highest price they can because they earn commission by doing so. Now, there is always room to negotiate so that the overall payment fits within your budget. Also, when purchasing a car, take into consideration the car insurance. You can do this by the make and model of the car you are looking to purchase and call the car insurance company to get a quote on the rate. Also, consider the type of gas you may have to use for the car. You may need to use Premium gas, which could be a determining factor when deciding on a car.

When purchasing a home, some of the same things apply like we talked about when purchasing a car, such as your credit, managing your money, and negotiating the price. One extra extremely important component of home purchasing is getting the right team. The right team includes:

- Real estate agent
- Mortgage loan officer
- Inspector
- Attorney

You want to make sure you do your independent research before securing each. Also, if this is your first home, there are a lot of first time homebuyer programs available that can help towards the down payment that you need to make to secure the home. The other important financial factor of home buying is the closing cost. There are programs that include them, you need to research them prior.

"The best preparation for tomorrow is doing your best today." - H. Jackson Brown, Jr.

> "Success is not final, failure is not fatal: it is the courage to continue that counts." - Winston Churchill

_____

_____

_____

_____

_____

_____

_____

_____

_____

_____

_____

_____

_____

_____

_____

_____

_____

_____

_____

_____

_____

_____

_____

"A bargain is something you can't use at a price you can't resist." Franklin Jones

_____

_____

_____

_____

_____

_____

_____

_____

_____

_____

_____

_____

_____

_____

_____

_____

_____

_____

_____

$ PAYING BILLS

There are two options for you to find out how much you owe for your bills. You can opt to have the paper statement sent to you monthly or choose to have it online with a notification going to your e-mail. For revolving credit such as credit cards and mortgage (the monthly payment for your house), it will have your credit limit how much you utilized for that month or the prior month with your remaining balance, due date, interest rate, and any applicable fees. It's important that you are aware of the due date, so that you do not pay bills late, which can impact your credit and, in most cases, incur a fee. Please note the payment should be made to the credit card company not the store for which you

CHASEFREEDOM® Manage your account online: www.chase.com/creditcards   Additional contact information conveniently located on reverse side

ACCOUNT SUMMARY

Previous Balance	$360.75
Payment, Credits	-$360.75
Purchases	+$507.35
New Balance	$507.35
Opening/Closing Date	
Total Credit Line	$11,000
Available Credit	$10,492
Cash Access Line	$2,200
Available for Cash	$2,200

PAYMENT INFORMATION

New Balance	$507.35
Payment Due Date	07/24/10
Minimum Payment Due	$10.00

Late Payment Warning: If we do not receive your minimum payment by the date listed above, you may have to pay up to a $39.00 late fee and your APRs will be subject to increase to a maximum Penalty APR of 29.99%.

Minimum Payment Warning: If you make only the minimum payment each period, you will pay more in interest and it will take you longer to pay off your balance. For example:

If you make no additional charges using this card and each month you pay	You will pay off the balance shown on this statement in about	And you will end up paying an estimated total of
Only the minimum payment	7 years	$849
$18	3 years	$645 (Savings=$204)

If you would like information about credit counseling services, call 1-866-797-2885.

made the purchase unless the credit card is from that store. Review the sample credit card statement included in this chapter.

There are also other bills if you rent an apartment or purchase a home or condo. Those can include the light bill, gas bill, water bill, heating, and trash. These are bills you will get on a monthly basis, but you do not have a credit limit. It will simply tell you how much you used, the amount due of what you used, and the due date. These are typically bills that do not show on your credit report, but you should still have a habit of paying them on time. They too can be mailed to you or viewed online. If you want a paper copy, then it will cost more. I encourage you to have some sort of filing or budget, so you know when they are due and how much you owe.

TIPS: 1. Pay your bills on time each month. 2. Try to pay the entire balance each month. 3. If you are unable to pay the entire balance be sure to never carry more that 30% of the credit limit.

Write down all of your monthly bills:

_____

_____

_____

_____

_____

_____

_____

_____

"Let no debt remain outstanding except the continuing debt to love on another." - Romans 13:8

_____

_____

_____

_____

_____

_____

_____

_____

_____

_____

_____

_____

_____

_____

_____

_____

_____

_____

_____

_____

> "The rich rules over the poor, and the borrower is the slave of the lender." - Proverbs 22:7

"It's one thing to learn what to do, it's another thing to execute - let's go." - Patrina Dixon

_____

_____

_____

_____

_____

_____

_____

_____

_____

_____

_____

_____

_____

_____

_____

_____

_____

_____

_____

_____

GAMING

As I did lectures and workshops across the world with young adults, I was asked to add this chapter in the book. From what I understand, many grapple with this when they start to earn their own money. Before I share the story of a young man I interviewed, who is now 19 lived in NY and now lives in MA, let me share some statistics on gaming and its negative financial impact:

> *How much money does a person spend on video games?* Online battle arena, role-playing and combat games all draw heavy spending through in-game purchases. Some 63.3% of gamers who have spent money on sports games have spent more than $100 on in-game purchases — the largest share of any game type.

> *What do gamers spend their money on?* The average PC gamer is likely to spend more money on cosmetics, characters, and weapon skins compared to the average mobile or console gamer. But mobile gaming revenue is higher than PC gaming revenue, because of the sheer volume of mobile gamers who match PC and console combined.

More information here:

https://www.forbes.com/sites/mattgardner1/2020/05/08/peo
ple-are-spending-ridiculous-time-and-money-on-gaming-during-
coronavirus/?sh=639460d432fe

Jay's story:

I was around 15-16 years of age, when I first started adventuring into the gaming atmosphere. In the beginning, I started watching gamers rage and become frustrated with whatever game they were playing, to now experiencing that same level of frustration and anger. The first game I had purchased was from a GameStop located in the Bronx, and it was NBA 2k17. Before the actual game is released for the world to play, GameStop allows you to pre-order the game. Now you could pre-order two types of editions, the standard edition ($60), Legend edition ($70), and the Legend edition gold ($100). I opted for the standard edition, as it was the cheaper option. This was in fact my first mistake. When you preorder this game, it also comes with free in-game content such as Virtual currency, clothes, shoes for your player, and team jerseys. The Legend edition gave you much more content even though it was a little higher price. In the standard edition, you would only receive 5,000 VC and a 90 overall Paul George Free agent card.

The regular Legend Edition received 30,000 VC and a 99 overall Kobe Bryant Free agent card and three My team Packs, while also coming with skins for your gaming controller and clothes within the game. Lastly, with the purchase of the Legend Gold Edition, you received an Additional 70,000 VC (Receives 100,000 VC in total) while also receiving 99 overall Michael Jordan and Kobe Bryant with a total five My team packs and 24 pairs of Kobe Bryant's shoes.

Now, the mistake I had made was purchasing the regular edition thinking I wouldn't need the extra in-game content. However, in order to fully upgrade your player to an 85 overall, it takes about 190,000 virtual currencies. Since I had purchased the Standard edition of the game, I had to make up around 185,000 worth of VC, which in real dollars amounted to $50. If I would've purchased the legend gold edition not only, would I only have to spend $20 additional dollars

(75,000 VC), I would've gotten a bunch of other features for free that only limited people received. But instead in order for me to receive this in-game content I would have to purchase more VC to buy the items required, which in turn lead me to spending a lot more money. On average, I was spending around $20-$40 a week on in-game purchases that were unnecessary and could've been avoided had I gone a different route in the beginning. This was unconventional as well because I was only 15-16 years of age with no steady income because I was under the age required to get a job.

Looking back on it now, I am glad that I found a different way to operate without having to spend so much money on in-game purchases. Instead of me spending money on in-game purchases, I now instead play a lot of game modes to generate VC to stop spending money (My career, Play Now6, Allstar-Team up, and playing against friends online). Altogether, my real problem spending money frivolously was on in-game purchases that I now deem as useless. I was able to eliminate this expense from my wallet successfully.

"What you get by achieving your goals is not as important as what you become by achieving your goals." - Zig Ziglar

_____

_____

_____

_____

_____

_____

_____

_____

_____

_____

_____

_____

_____

_____

_____

_____

_____

_____

_____

"Believe you can and you're halfway there." - Theodore Roosevelt

"You got this! - Patrina Dixon

It'$ My Money

_____

_____

_____

_____

_____

_____

_____

_____

_____

_____

_____

_____

_____

_____

_____

_____

_____

_____

_____

_____

_____

_____

_____

ENTREPRENEURSHIP OR SIDE HUSTLES

There is a difference between owning your own business, even if it is on the side, and having a side hustle. It is a business when it's set-up structurally, and a side hustle when it's something you do occasionally, like selling cupcakes or pies during the holidays or cutting or braiding hair on college campus. You get paid for your product or service and you are on your merry way. Your side hustle can turn to a business.

When you want to set up a business structurally.

You **need** to:
- Choose a business name. Check with your state to ensure no other business have that same name.
- You want to determine which kind of business entity you will have, sole proprietorship or LLC. You can review the various types online
- Then you want to get an Employer Identification Number (EIN). There isn't a cost for this
- Then you want to register your business with your state. There is a cost for this, and it varies by state.
- Open a business bank account.
- Let people know you are in business and what you do. There maybe be costs associated with this depending on how you choose to let people know about your business.
- Create a business plan.

You want to do research on the business you want to start. Know who you are selling to or who will be your target customers. How do they get their information? Those are the places you want to market your business.

Also, understand your friends and family will not be your forever customers. They will certainly support you when you get started. Think about it if they have gotten your product or service they will not be continued customers.

Be able to describe how the business solves a need to those that need the solution. Your research will give you some of this, but you have to continue this process regularly.

Other steps are **encouraged**:
- Create a social media page - no cost (keep in mind not everyone is on social media)
- Then graduate to a website (this varies by type of business) - cost varies as you have to buy the domain, the hosting site, then either build the website yourself or have someone else build it and then you can choose for them to maintain it or show you how to maintain it.
- The two above are what I call the 24 hours a day, 7 days a week, 365 days a year business card for the business. When you are asleep, people from other countries are able to learn about your business and you if you have a place such as a website to get the information.

Being an entrepreneur is a lot of work but very rewarding. There is a sample business plan on the next page.

IT'$ MY MONEY BUSINESS PLAN

What is your idea?

_____

_____

Is it a product? A service?

_____

What makes your idea unique?

_____

_____

What do existing products/services not offer that yours will?

_____

_____

Why will people buy it?

_____

_____

Name:

_____

What does this name say about your business?

_____

_____

Is it unique? Memorable? Easy to pronounce?

_____

85

MARKETING:

Who will be your customers?
Are they adults? Kids? Teens? Men? Women?

_____

_____

Where do they live? _____

_____

Describe your target customer with as much detail as you know.

_____

_____

_____

_____

_____

Where will you sell your product or service?

_____

_____

_____

_____

How will you get the word out about your business?

_____

_____

_____

Will you email your friends?

_____

STARTUP COSTS:

How many TT will it cost to start your business?

_____

_____

What will you need to buy before you can get started? Materials?

_____

_____

Equipment? How much TT will those things cost?

_____

_____

Where will you get the TT?

_____

_____

PRICING:

How much TT will you charge?

_____

_____

How does your pricing compare to your competitors?

_____

_____

"The sky is no longer the limit, it is only the view." – Taraji P. Henson.

"Dream, Dream, Dream. Execute on what you learn and you can achieve." Patrina Dixon

_____

_____

_____

_____

_____

_____

_____

_____

_____

_____

_____

_____

_____

_____

_____

_____

_____

_____

_____

"When they go low, we go high." - Mrs. Michele Obama

Understanding the value of money, importance of financial stability, and how you plan and act on those plans, serve as the road for the financial success you want ahead.

I know you may be asking yourself:
- What do I do with all of this information?
- How do I use it in my everyday life?
- What are your next steps?

The next important step is to EXECUTE! It is also important to continue to educate yourself on financial topics. Surround yourself with individuals who inspire and motivate you on your financial journey. Ask questions. Create better daily money habits. Remember, if you make a mistake, no problem, learn from it and keep going forward.

Review your journal entries regularly. Have your thoughts and plans progressed? What is one accomplishment you can celebrate? What is one item you can commit to working on?

Stay tuned for It'$ My Money Volume 3.

RESOURCES

FAFSA Application source-
http://fafsapplication.org/after-completing-the-
fafsa/federal-student-aid-refunds/

Free Credit Reports
www.annualcreditreport.com

Free Budget Sheet
www.itsmymoneyjournal.info/resources

Free Debt Tracker
www.itsmymoneyjournal.info/resources

The Money Exchange Podcast
On audio platforms including Pandora

YouTube:
It's My Money with Patrina Dixon

Compare Credit Cards
www.nerdwallet.com or www.bankrate.com

Free Credit Score
www.experian.com

GLOSSARY

401K: Retirement savings plan sponsored by the employer.

Account balance: The amount available in our saving or checking account.

Account fee: The fee a bank or credit union charges for their account certain services or for misuse of the account

Automated teller machine (ATM): A machine with a computer that is used to make deposits, withdraws, account balances and transfers using a debit or credit card.

Bad check: A check that will not be paid by the bank because the account does not have enough money in it. Also known as a bounced or returned check. Banks and other companies typically charge an additional fee when this happens.

Bank: A financial institution that handles money, accounts, loans, and additional financial services.

Bank account: A service provided by the bank to keep track of your money, how it is handled, and tracked. Most banks offer a variety of types of accounts.

Bank statement: A document that list all of the transactions on your bank account. Deposits, withdrawals, etc...

Certificate of deposit (CD): An account offered by a bank or credit union where the funds must stay for a specific amount of time. A penalty fee will be applied if the funds are taken out prior to the agreed upon date.

Check: An official written document giving the bank or credit union permission to pay a desired amount to a specific person, company, or store.

Checking account: As account that allows you to deposit and withdraw money, write checks, and use a debit card to access your funds.

Compound interest: The total amount your account earns based on the initial deposit and the interest earned over time.

Debit card: The card associated with a checking or saving account; it can be used to make deposits or withdraws.

Debt: Money, goods, or services you owe to others.

Deposit: When you put money into your account.

Deposit slip: The slip you complete and provide to the teller in the bank or credit union to add money to a bank account.

Discretionary expense: Items, goods, purchases, or services that are not considered a need. Examples include shopping, extra activities, and savings.

Earning power: The amount of income, or money, a person can make from working or providing a service.

Expense: Items, goods, purchases, or services. Examples include shopping, outings or eating out.

Fixed expense: An expense that does not change, usually the same every month such as rent, mortgage or car payment.

Flexible expense: An expense that varies from time to time, amount spent, or based on need such as groceries, clothes, or gas.

FDIC: Federal Deposit Insurance Corporation. Insures up to $250,000 in banks, per depositor, per bank, per category.

Income: The amount of money you have coming in. Usually form working.

Interest: The amount of money the borrower pays the lender in exchange for using the lender's funds.

Investing: Using funds to buy ownership, product, stocks, real estate or other items of value with hopes of earning a profit (more money) over a period of time.

Investment: The product, stock, property, or possession that is purchased for profit.

Minimum balance: The minimum amount needed to open specific accounts at a bank or credit union.

NCUA: National Credit Union Administration insures up to $250,000 in credit unions, per depositor, per credit union, per category.

Non-sufficient funds (NSF): Not enough money in your account to pay a check to charge to your account.

Online banking: Ability to monitor your banking transactions, access your accounts, and perform other services using a computer, cell phone or app.

Overdraft: When money is withdrawn from your account that is greater than the available balance. The bank usually charges an additional penalty fee.

Personal identification number (PIN): A four-digit secret combination used to gain access to your accounts using a debit or credit card.

Portfolio: A range of investments held by a person or organization

Routing number: A nine-digit number at the bottom of your checks used to identify which bank or credit union issued the check.

Sales tax: An additional charge by the state or city on the item purchased.

Savings account: An account that allows you to earn interest while monitoring your funds, allowing for deposits and withdraws.

Simple interest: The amount of money earned based on the original amount deposited.

Stock: Ownership in a company.

Withdraw: To take money out of your account.

Withdrawal slip: A slip that you must complete to identify an account so money can be taken out.

CONTACT PATRINA

Website: www.itsmymoneyjournal.info

Instagram, Twitter, TikTok and Pinterest: @itsmymoney_

The Money Exchange Podcast
On audio platforms including Pandora

YouTube:
It's My Money with Patrina Dixon

FaceBook Community: The It'$ My Money Squad

Go to **www.itsmymoneyjournal.info** and
sign up to receive weekly newsletters